Kings & Queens to colour

Illustrated by Sophie Crichton
Written by Ruth Brocklehurst
Designed by Ian McNee

Usborne Quicklinks
For links to websites where you can find out more about British kings and queens, go to the Usborne Quicklinks
Website at www.usborne.com/quicklinks and type the keywords 'Kings and Queens to colour'.
Please read our internet safety guidelines on the Usborne Quicklinks Website.

Edgar the Peaceful

In 973, Edgar the Peaceful was crowned King of England. In those days, the rest of Britain was divided into smaller kingdoms with their own kings. As part of Edgar's coronation, these kings had to swear loyalty to him, and were said to have rowed him along the River Dee.

Edgar steered the boat to show that he had power over the other kings.

As many as eight British rulers swore loyalty to Edgar.

Edgar's palace at the city of Chester

Royal Orders

In 1348, Edward III founded a society called the Order of the Garter to reward his most loyal knights. It still exists today, and is the highest royal order that the Queen awards for service to Britain.

This is the Greater George Badge, worn by Knights of the Garter.

Here, Edward III wears the blue Garter Robe with the Garter Badge. In the middle of the badge is the red cross of St. George on a white background.

St. George, the patron saint of the Order, is shown slaying a dragon.

Knights wear a blue garter below their left knees, and ladies wear it on their left arms.

This shield shows Edward III's special symbols, or 'coat of arms'.

Every June, members of the Order of the Garter attend a service at St. George's Chapel, in Windsor Castle. Each member's seat in the chapel is topped with his or her own crest.

The crests are carved from wood and brightly painted.

This crest shows a mythical creature called a griffin.

A royal feast

Richard II, who ruled England in 1377-1399, created a magnificent court for himself. He loved dressing in fine clothes, and gave lavish feasts to impress his guests.

We know what was served at Richard's feasts because his chef described it all in a recipe book.

In this scene, the King and Queen sit in the middle, with their most important guests on either side.

This servant is carrying a 'cockatrice' — half beast, half fowl.

This man is serving a dish made to look like a castle.

Feasts consisted of three substantial courses. To entertain the diners, cooks created elaborate dishes, called 'subtleties', that were made to look like something else – from mythical creatures to ships or castles.

Richard's clothes were often lined with fur and embroidered with gold thread.

Diners ate with knives, spoons and their fingers.

Henry VIII at the Field of the Cloth of Gold

Henry VIII was accompanied by the first of his six wives, Catherine of Aragon.

Henry VIII enjoyed showing off his wealth and athletic skills. In 1520, he met Francis I, King of France, to celebrate peace between their nations. The festivities went on for 11 days of extravagant feasts, sports and games.

The event got its name because many of the tents, and the kings' outfits, were made from gold cloth.

Francis I's horse wore a blue and gold cloth.

Elizabeth I at Tilbury

In 1588, the King of Spain sent a vast fleet of warships, called an armada, to attack England. Queen Elizabeth I gathered her soldiers at Tilbury, on the southeast coast. There, she gave a rousing speech, promising to fight alongside them if Spanish forces invaded.

English ship flying white flags with red crosses

"I know I have the body of a weak and feeble woman; but I have the heart and stomach of a king, and a king of England too."

Part of Elizabeth's speech.

The English fleet defeated the Spanish armada, and the invasion was called off. But Elizabeth's speech showed she was a brave warrior queen.

Red and yellow
striped flags

Spanish ship

Elizabeth I's
coat of arms

Scottish kings and queens

Until the 17th century, Scotland and England had their own royal families, and the two kingdoms were often at war with each other.

Robert the Bruce fought hard for Scotland's independence from England. Here, he wears a red lion on a yellow background.

Robert the Bruce
reigned 1306-1329

James IV ended hostilities with England by marrying Margaret Tudor, daughter of Henry VII of England.

James IV
reigned 1488-1513

In this portrait, James is shown holding a falcon, which he would have used to hunt with.

Margaret Tudor

Mary Queen
of Scots

Mary Queen of Scots
was accused of plotting
against Elizabeth I of
England, who had her
executed in 1587.

James VI

Both Mary and
Elizabeth I were
granddaughters of
Henry VII. In 1603,
Elizabeth died childless
and was succeeded by
Mary's son, James VI.

James VI of Scotland
became James I of England
but the two kingdoms
remained separate.

Charles I and Henrietta Maria

Charles I was a fun-loving king. He and his queen, Henrietta Maria, held lavish theatrical performances called masques, at their royal palaces.

Charles I was King of England, Scotland and Ireland from 1625 to 1649. He and Henrietta Maria are shown here dressed in the latest fashions of the day.

The Queen was fond of bright silk dresses trimmed with expensive lace and lots of pearls.

Masques involved music, poetry and dancing, with spectacular stage sets designed by leading artists and plays written by famous writers.

Performers, guests, and sometimes even the King and Queen, dressed in amazing costumes for court masques.

Glittering crowns

The most impressive items worn by kings and queens are their crowns. They are incredibly valuable, and are powerful symbols of royal authority.

St. Edward's Crown is the official coronation crown. It was made in 1661 from gold that may have come from a crown belonging to Edward the Confessor, who died in 1066.

The **Imperial State Crown** is set with over 3,000 gems. It was used for Queen Victoria's Coronation, in 1838, and remade for George VI, in 1937, because both felt the St. Edward's Crown was too heavy.

The huge gemstone in the middle is a red spinel. Below it is a massive diamond.

Both of these crowns have purple velvet linings with white ermine fur borders.

Circlet with alternating crosses and fleurs-de-lys encrusted with diamonds, rubies, pearls, emeralds and sapphires

The **Crown of Scotland** was used to crown Scottish kings and queens until the 17th century.

Made from Scottish gold set with precious stones and freshwater pearls, this crown has a red velvet lining.

Gold crown with purple velvet lining

Alternating crosses and fleurs-de-lys

The **Tudor Crown**, worn by Henry VIII and his successors, was destroyed in 1649, after Charles I was dethroned and executed.

The **Coronet of the Prince of Wales** was made in 1969 for Prince Charles. Although it's based on traditional designs, its style is very modern.

Queen Anne in her sedan

In 1707, England and Scotland were united as a single kingdom called Great Britain under Queen Anne. She was a popular, hard-working queen, but suffered a lot of ill-health. Walking was so painful that she often was carried in a sedan chair instead.

The trumpeter wears a traditional coat called a tabard. It is decorated with Queen Anne's coat of arms: three gold fleurs-de-lys on a blue background, three gold lions 'passant guardant' on red, a single red lion 'rampant' on gold and a gold harp on blue.

In this scene, Queen Anne is being carried in a sedan chair to a service in Westminster Abbey, in London.

Sedan chairs were a popular way to get around cities in the 18th century.

The men wear white powdered wigs and three-cornered 'tricorn' hats. Their jackets, known as frock coats, have brass buttons and are edged with gold braid.

The Queen is being carried by footmen in red frock coats.

Mr and Mrs King

King George III reigned from 1760 to 1820. He and his wife, Queen Charlotte, had 15 children, and tried to lead a normal, happy family life. They jokingly called each other Mr and Mrs King.

Prince George succeeded his father, first as Prince Regent, then as King George IV.

Prince Frederick became an army general when he grew up, and was made Duke of York.

Prince Edward, playing with the family's pet spaniel, wears a dress. This was the custom for all boys and girls under four years old.

Prince William became King William IV at the age of 62. Here, he is holding his pet parrot.

In this scene, the royal family is posing for a portrait in 17th-century costumes, but George III is wearing a white, powdered wig, fashionable in the 1770s.

George III

Princess Augusta

Queen Charlotte

Princess Charlotte

Royal animals

From around 1210 to 1832, the Tower of London housed the Royal Menagerie – filled with exotic animals that were mostly gifts from foreign rulers.

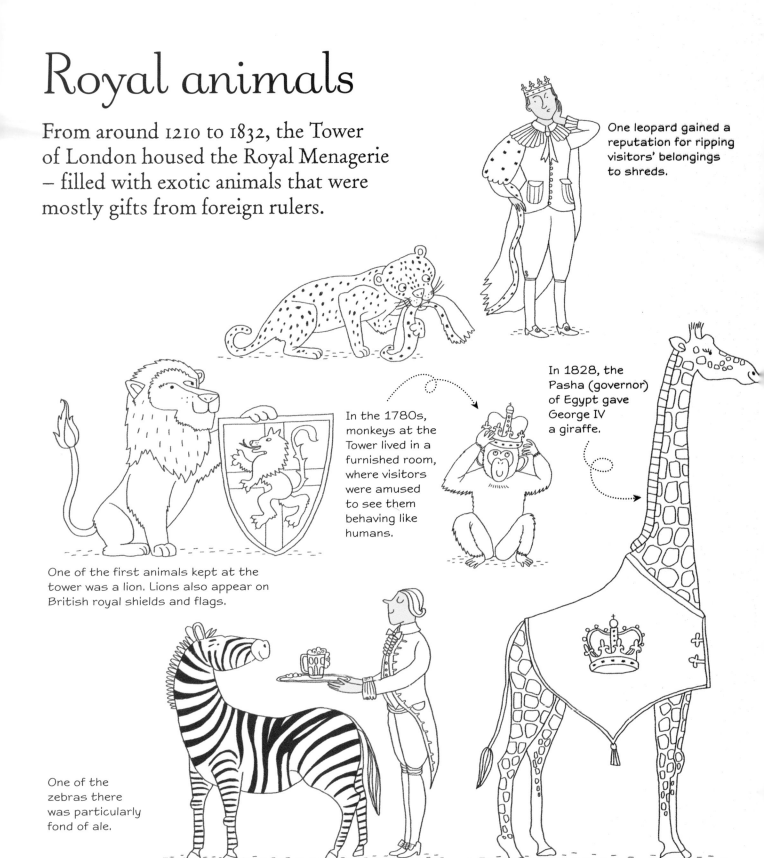

One leopard gained a reputation for ripping visitors' belongings to shreds.

In the 1780s, monkeys at the Tower lived in a furnished room, where visitors were amused to see them behaving like humans.

In 1828, the Pasha (governor) of Egypt gave George IV a giraffe.

One of the first animals kept at the tower was a lion. Lions also appear on British royal shields and flags.

One of the zebras there was particularly fond of ale.

Over the centuries, many British kings and queens have kept animals as much-loved pets. Today, most members of the Royal Family are involved with animal charities, too.

Queen Victoria and her family had several pets, including love birds and a parrot as well as dogs and horses.

Mary Queen of Scots had a Skye terrier. It was so devoted to her, it was found whimpering under her skirt at her execution.

Charles I and Henrietta Maria were the first British King and Queen to include their dogs, Cavalier King Charles spaniels, in royal portraits.

Edward VII's wire fox terrier, Caesar, was so important to the King that he walked behind the King's coffin in his funeral procession.

Elizabeth II had her first pet corgi when she was 7. She has had corgis ever since, and sometimes takes them with her to public events.

Queen Victoria's Coronation

Victoria was only 19 years old when she was crowned Queen of England in 1838. The Coronation was held at Westminster Abbey, with a splendid procession through the streets of London. Around 400,000 people gathered to cheer for the new Queen.

Cavalry officers in red coats with gold trim

This is the Captain of the Yeomen of the Guard, the royal bodyguards.

Red jacket

This officer is a royal bodyguard whose title is the Gold Stick after the ceremonial stick he carries.

Gold State Coach

This Yeoman carries an ornamental spear. He is wearing a black hat, red stockings and a red tunic with gold braid.

Gold stick

Black shoes with red, white and blue rosettes

The Delhi Durbar

In 1911, a ten-day ceremony, or *durbar*, was held in the Indian city of Delhi to celebrate the coronation of George V and Queen Mary as Emperor and Empress of India.

The celebrations included a massive military procession with dignitaries riding on brightly decorated elephants.

George V wore the Imperial Crown of India, which contains more than 6,000 diamonds.

Queen Mary wore a diamond and emerald necklace, given to her on behalf of the ladies of India.

These soldiers wear white turbans and leggings with red tunics.

The King and Queen appeared in their coronation robes. All of India's most important princes and officials came to pay their respects.

Coronation costumes

Elizabeth II's Coronation, in 1953, was the first to be broadcast on television, watched by more than 20 million people around the world.

Everyone involved in the ceremony wore traditional costumes.

Peers (lords) wore their red robes over black velvet suits with white bowties.

The Earl Marshal wore white breeches, and a short gold jacket called a coatee under his robe.

Peeresses (ladies) wore ivory gowns.

All of the robes were made of deep red velvet, trimmed with white ermine fur.

The Royal Pages of Honour wore red tunics with blue cuffs and gold trim.

These two outfits were worn over white silk breeches and stockings.

The Garter King of Arms wore a tabard (tunic) decorated with the Queen's coat of arms.

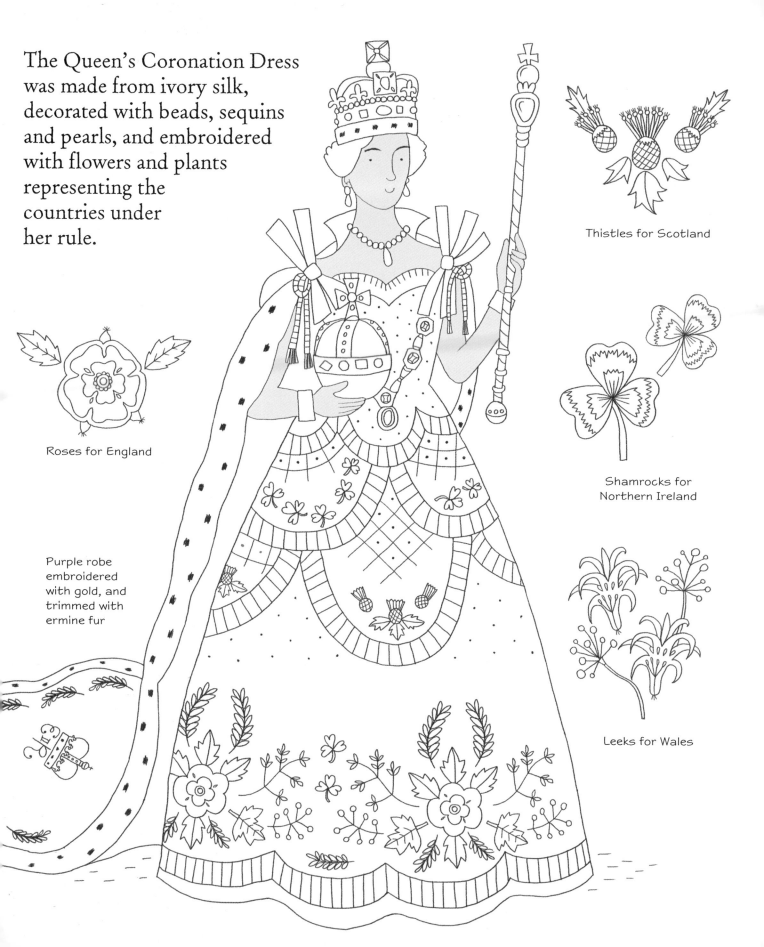

The Queen's Coronation Dress was made from ivory silk, decorated with beads, sequins and pearls, and embroidered with flowers and plants representing the countries under her rule.

Roses for England

Purple robe embroidered with gold, and trimmed with ermine fur

Thistles for Scotland

Shamrocks for Northern Ireland

Leeks for Wales

Royal jewels

The Queen has a stunning collection of priceless jewels. These include brooches, necklaces and tiaras that the Queen and other female members of the royal family wear at formal occasions.

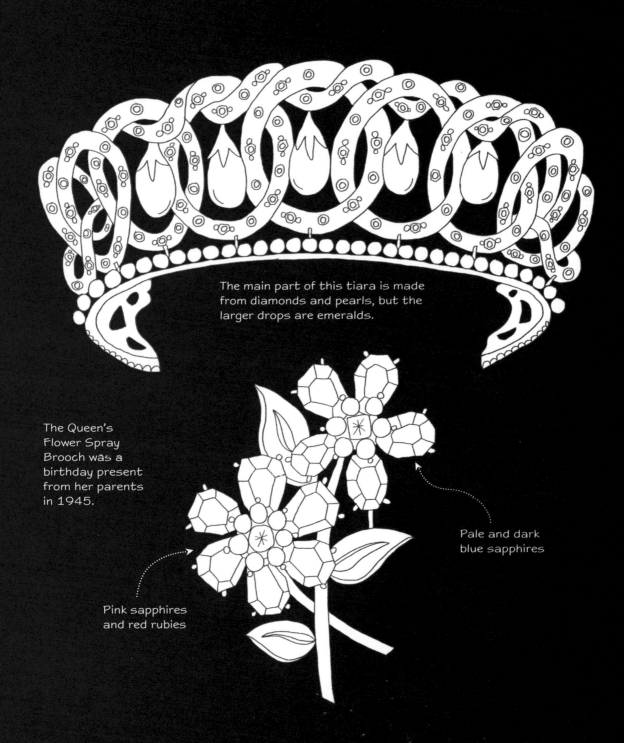

The main part of this tiara is made from diamonds and pearls, but the larger drops are emeralds.

The Queen's Flower Spray Brooch was a birthday present from her parents in 1945.

Pale and dark blue sapphires

Pink sapphires and red rubies

This is the 'Ladies of India' Necklace, given to Queen Mary at the Delhi Durbar. It is made from diamonds and bright green emeralds and was worn with matching earrings.

The Queen's Jardiniere Brooch is set with sapphire flowers, red ruby berries and emerald leaves.

The Queen Mother's Leaf Brooch is set with diamonds and blue, green, red and purple gems.

The lion and the unicorn

The lion and the unicorn both appear in the full royal coat of arms, and are often shown as flag bearers.

The English flag is a red cross on a white background.

The lion is gold and stands for England.

The Scottish flag is a white cross on a blue background.

The Unicorn is silver and stands for Scotland.